DISCOVERING

GREAT BRITAIN

By Philip Steele

A *ZOË BOOK*

© 1994 Zoë Books Limited

Devised and produced by
Zoë Books Limited
15 Worthy Lane
Winchester
Hampshire SO23 7AB
England

First published in Great Britain in 1994 by
Zoë Books Limited
15 Worthy Lane
Winchester
Hampshire SO23 7AB

A record of the CIP data is available from the British Library.

ISBN 1 874488 24 X

Printed in Italy by Grafedit SpA
Design: Jan Sterling, Sterling Associates
Picture research: Victoria Sturgess
Map: Gecko Limited
Production: Grahame Griffiths

Photographic acknowledgments
The publishers wish to acknowledge, with thanks, the following photographic sources:

Cover: Robert Harding Picture Library; title page: Robert Harding Picture Library; 5l Impact Photos/Chris Kelly; 5r Magma, Anglesey; 6 Robert Harding Picture Library; 7l DDA Photo Library: 7r & 8 Robert Harding Picture Library; 9l Zefa; 9r Robert Harding Picture Library; 10 Serpentine Design; 11l Robert Eames; 11r Magma, Anglesey; 12 David Williams Picture Library; 13l British Petroleum; 13r David Williams Picture Library; 14 & 15l DDA Photo Library; 15r Robert Harding Picture Library; 16 DDA Photo Library; 17l Courtesy of ICI Chemicals & Polymers Ltd; 17r Magma, Anglesey; 18 Robert Harding Picture Library; 19l DDA Photo Library; 19r David Williams Picture Library; 20 Greg Evans International; 21l DDA Photo Library; 21r Greg Evans International; 22 Sporting Pictures; 23l Catherine Ashmore; 23r Charles Tait; 24 Robert Harding Picture Library; 25l Ancient Art & Architecture Collection; 25r York Archaeological Trust Picture Library; 26 Ancient Art & Architecture Collection; 27l Zefa; 27r Robert Harding Picture Library; 28 Mary Evans Picture Library; 29l Peter Newark's Military Pictures; 29r Tony Stone Images

Cover: *The Houses of Parliament, in London*

Title page: *Edinburgh Castle*

Contents

Welcome to Britain!   5

South and East   6

The heart of England   8

The West and Wales   10

North of the border   12

London   14

People at work   16

Everyday life   18

Food and drink   20

Leisure and arts   22

Back into history   24

Wars and revolts   26

Into the modern world   28

Fact file   30

Index   32

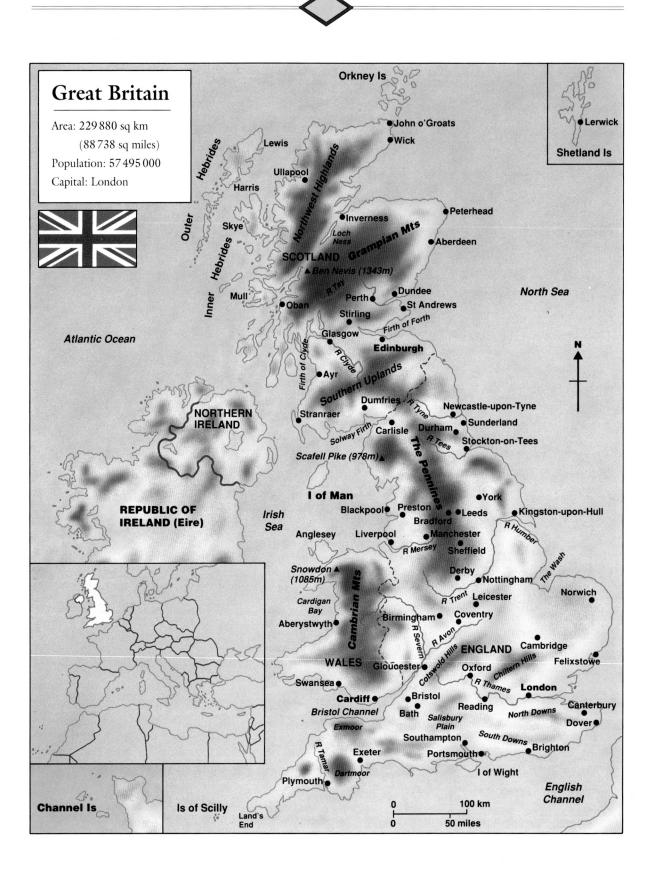

Great Britain

Area: 229 880 sq km
(88 738 sq miles)
Population: 57 495 000
Capital: London

Orkney Is

John o'Groats

Wick

Lerwick

Shetland Is

Hebrides

Lewis

Ullapool

Harris

Skye

Inverness

Peterhead

Outer

Loch
Ness

Grampian Mts

Aberdeen

Hebrides

SCOTLAND

Northwest Highlands

▲ Ben Nevis (1343m)

North Sea

Inner

Mull

R Tay

Perth

Dundee

St Andrews

Oban

Stirling

Firth of Forth

Atlantic Ocean

Glasgow

R Clyde

Edinburgh

N

Firth of Clyde

Ayr

Southern Uplands

NORTHERN
IRELAND

Dumfries

R Tyne

Newcastle-upon-Tyne

Stranraer

Carlisle

Durham

Sunderland

Solway Firth

Stockton-on-Tees

Scafell Pike (978m) ▲

The Pennines

REPUBLIC OF
IRELAND (Eire)

I of Man

York

Irish
Sea

Blackpool

Preston

Leeds

Kingston-upon-Hull

Bradford

Anglesey

Liverpool

Manchester

R Humber

R Mersey

Sheffield

The Wash

Snowdon ▲
(1085m)

Derby

Cambrian Mts

Nottingham

Norwich

Cardigan
Bay

R Trent

Leicester

Aberystwyth

Birmingham

Coventry

R Severn

R Avon

ENGLAND

Cambridge

Chiltern Hills

Felixstowe

WALES

Gloucester

Cotswold Hills

Oxford

Swansea

R Thames

London

Cardiff

Bristol

Reading

Canterbury

Bristol Channel

Bath

North Downs

Dover

Exmoor

Salisbury
Plain

South Downs

Brighton

R Tamar

Exeter

Southampton

Portsmouth

Dartmoor

I of Wight

English
Channel

Plymouth

Channel Is

Is of Scilly

Land's
End

0   100 km

0   50 miles

Welcome to Britain!

The British Isles lie off the northwest coast of Europe. To the east are the shallow waters of the North Sea. To the west are the deep, stormy waters of the Atlantic Ocean. Ocean winds and currents keep the climate mild and moist, particularly in the west. It is often said that people here talk about the weather more than any other subject!

Great Britain is the largest of the British Isles. It is made up of three countries – England, Scotland and Wales. These belong to a single nation known as the United Kingdom (UK). The nation is divided into smaller regions called counties.

Ireland is the second largest of the British Isles. Ireland (Eire) is an independent nation, but the six counties of Ulster, in Northern Ireland, are governed as a province of the United

A ferry arrives at the English Channel port of Dover.

Stormy weather over Snowdonia, in Wales

Kingdom. Information about Northern Ireland is not included in this book.

Britain and Europe

A narrow strip of sea called the English Channel separates Great Britain from the European mainland. However, a new rail tunnel will soon connect England with France. Since 1973 the United Kingdom has been a member of the European Community (EC), and has developed closer links with its mainland neighbours.

South and East

Much of the south and the east of England is rich farmland. The county of Kent was once known as the 'garden of England', because of its orchards and hop fields. Sheep graze the South Downs, a range of chalk hills in Sussex. In recent years grapevines have been planted on the North Downs, in Surrey.

The region has many fine old towns. Christian pilgrims have been coming to the shrine of St Thomas à Becket in the cathedral city of Canterbury for more than 800 years. Canterbury is the centre of the Church of England (the Anglican Church).

The ancient university city of Oxford lies to the west, near the head of the Thames Valley. The River Thames flows eastwards through London to the North Sea.

The south and east have always been wealthy regions and are densely populated. Many people who work in the commercial centre of London live in the area around the capital, known as the Home Counties. Here, many small towns have been swallowed up by the sprawling suburbs of London.

Motorways now cut through the woods and fields. Aircraft take off from the three international airports which serve London – Heathrow, Gatwick and Stansted.

Devil's Dyke is a part of the South Downs, a range of rounded, green hills in southeast England.

Heading down the Channel

England's south coast has chalk cliffs and shingle beaches. Large holiday resorts such as Brighton and Bournemouth are found on the south coast.

Many visitors to Britain arrive at ferry ports such as Harwich and Dover. Portsmouth and Southampton are also major centres of international shipping. Yachts and pleasure boats head for the Isle of Wight, which lies across the waters of the Solent.

Southern landscapes include the open expanse of Salisbury Plain and the leafy villages of the New Forest, famous for its ponies and deer. In Wiltshire and Dorset, many cottages and farmhouses still have thatched roofs.

A pony in the New Forest

The Channel Islands

Ferries leave the port of Weymouth for the Channel Islands. Guernsey, Jersey and their smaller neighbours lie off the coast of France, and a few people there still speak a French dialect, or *patois*. The islands have close links with Britain, but are not part of the United Kingdom.

Windmills are common landmarks on the Norfolk Broads.

Flat lands and fens

North of the Thames estuary, the coastline is low-lying and liable to flooding. This is a land of shallow lakes ('broads') and wetlands ('fens'). Much of the farmland has been drained from marshes.

East Anglia, which takes in the counties of Essex, Suffolk and Norfolk, is a flat region beneath wide open skies. It produces wheat, sugar beet and vegetable crops. In the Middle Ages it was famed for its trade in wool, and in its towns you can still see the fine half-timbered houses and large churches of that period. Today the quays of Felixstowe are stacked with export containers bound for Dutch and German ports.

Further west is the beautiful skyline of Cambridge. Like Oxford, the city is known for its ancient university. To the north, across the inlet of The Wash, rise the low chalk hills of the Lincolnshire Wolds.

The heart of England

Shakespeare's wife's cottage, Stratford-upon-Avon

Cities of the English Midlands include Wolverhampton and Coventry. The largest city, Birmingham, is home to more than a million people. Its sprawling suburbs are surrounded by so many motorways that one busy interchange is nicknamed 'Spaghetti Junction'!

The city grew up as a centre of engineering. Many of its factories have now closed, but the city remains an important business centre. In recent years it has become known for its classical music and ballet and also for the culture of its large Asian community.

Not all the Midlands region is industrial. To the south, the county of Warwickshire includes historical towns such as Stratford-upon-Avon, the birthplace of the greatest English playwright, William Shakespeare (1564-1616). To the west, the farmland and canals of Shropshire extend to the hills of the Welsh border.

To the east are the old manufacturing towns of Leicester and Nottingham, famous for the legend of Robin Hood. To the north lies Staffordshire, with its potteries and breweries. From here the River Trent flows northwards into Derbyshire, with its wooded valleys, or 'dales', and the rocky peaks of the Pennines. The city of Derby was once an important railway centre, and the home of Rolls Royce engine-building.

Across the Mersey

About 150 years ago industrial towns grew up all over the northwest of

Liverpool's old waterfront

England. Manchester was built with the wealth of the cotton industry. The mills of Lancashire exported textiles around the world. At the centre of the region was the great port of Liverpool on the River Mersey.

Industry and shipping have now declined. Liverpool has seen hard times, but the city is still famed for the spirit of its people. Liverpudlian humour was made world-famous by the Beatles pop group in the 1960s.

In the far northwest, Cumbria is a county of shining lakes and peaceful hills. The peak of Scafell Pike reaches a height of 978m (3210ft).

The Isle of Man

Man has had its own parliament, called the *Tynwald*, since the year AD 979. Today its low taxes have drawn many business people to the island. Some people speak the Celtic language of the island, and still maintain its ancient traditions. The island is well known for its annual motorcycle races and for the island's breed of tail-less cat, the Manx!

From Humber to Tyne

North Sea trawlers sail down the mouth of the River Humber from the ports of Grimsby and Hull. In the last ten years however, the fishing fleets have become smaller and other industries have developed in these towns. Yorkshire has beautiful, bleak moors and the fine city of York. There are also large industrial towns such as Leeds, Bradford and Sheffield.

The northeastern counties are known for their ancient abbeys, cathedrals and castles, such as Durham, on the River Wear, and Bamburgh, on the lonely Northumbrian coast. Industrial centres include Newcastle upon Tyne, Sunderland and Stockton-on-Tees. This region was once a centre of coalmining, railways and shipbuilding. Modern industries include chemicals and plastics.

Bamburgh Castle, guarding the northeast coast

The West and Wales

Cornish fishermen on the Lizard peninsula

Bristol's stone buildings rise high above the River Avon. Anchored in the docks is Brunel's *Great Britain*, the world's first screw-propeller steamship, built in the 1840s. The Bristol Channel extends westwards to the Atlantic Ocean. The elegant town of Bath takes its name from hot springs. The Romans once bathed here and called it *Aquae Sulis.*

England's West Country stretches from Herefordshire and Worcestershire down to Devon and Cornwall. It takes in the Cotswold Hills, farmland fields and orchards of cider-apples. In Somerset, the open hills of Exmoor are home to red deer and small sturdy ponies.

Cream and butter are produced by the farms of Devon. The rich green pastures rise to the lonely uplands of Dartmoor. The port of Plymouth is a large naval base.

Across the River Tamar lies Cornwall. This long, rocky peninsula stretches westwards towards the Scilly Isles. Its beautiful coastline and small fishing villages attract many visitors. Cornwall was once known for its tin mining, and still produces China clay. Place names show that Cornwall –*Kernow* in the Cornish language – shares the same cultural background as other Celtic lands such as Wales.

A rescue helicopter hovers over Snowdon.

Land of the Red Dragon

Across the Severn Bridge lies Wales (*Cymru*), one of the three countries of Great Britain. Its flag shows a red dragon on a green and white background. The 3 million people who live here have their own history and traditions. There are two official languages, English and Welsh. Welsh is spoken as first language by about half a million people, mostly in the north and west of Wales. Many people would like to see a separate Welsh assembly or parliament. Some wish to see Wales break away from the United Kingdom altogether, to become an independent nation within Europe.

The chief towns of south Wales are the capital, Cardiff (*Caerdydd*), and Swansea (*Abertawe*). The southern valleys are industrial. Most of their coalmines have been closed and replaced by other industries. Steel is produced at Llanwern and oil is refined at Milford Haven (*Aberdaugleddau*).

Mid-Wales and the northwest are taken up by range after range of beautiful mountains, reaching their highest point at Snowdon (*Yr Wyddfa*) at a height of 1085m (3560ft). Sheep graze the high pastures. The west coast sweeps past the university town of Aberystwyth to the Llŷn Peninsula. Northern roads take the traveller past castles and beaches to the industrialised banks of the River Dee (*Dyfrdwy*).

Bards and choirs

Welsh singers and poets compete at festivals called *eisteddfodau*. The national *eisteddfod*, held at a different site each year, is a favourite meeting place. There are also local and youth festivals. The international *eisteddfod* at Llangollen attracts dancers and musicians from all over the world.

A fanfare at the national eisteddfod, in Wales

North of the border

Scotland, like Wales, is a country with its own history and culture. It has its own laws, church and education system, while remaining part of the United Kingdom. Many of the 5 million population campaign for their own assembly or parliament in Edinburgh. Here, too, there are calls for independence.

The Gaelic language may still be heard, especially in the north and west. Some people speak Scots, a form of English which contains many words unknown south of the border.

Scotland's capital is Edinburgh, on the south bank of the Firth of Forth. Its castle towers over the stone-built city, linked to the palace of Holyrood House by the Royal Mile. Edinburgh is home to museums and art galleries, and each year there is a festival of the arts. Theatre groups, comedians, artists and musicians flock to Edinburgh from all over the world.

Scotland's largest city is Glasgow, 72km (45miles) to the west on the River Clyde. The busy days of Clyde shipbuilding are over. New buildings and motorways have now replaced much of the nineteenth-century housing, but the toughness and sharp humour for which Glaswegians are famous has remained.

Lowlands and highlands

The Borders region, crossed by the River Tweed, was once the site of cattle raids and battles between the Scots and the

A bagpipe band at the Strathallan Games

English. To the southwest are the hills and 'lochs' (lakes) of Dumfries and Galloway. Scotland's greatest poet, Robert Burns, was born near Ayr in 1759.

Further north are the beautiful ranges of the Grampian Mountains. Ben Nevis (*Beinn Nibheis*) at 1343m (4406ft) is the highest point in all the British Isles. The Caledonian Canal links the North Sea with the Atlantic Ocean, joining up a series of lochs in the Great Glen. Beyond lie the Northwest Highlands.

The Loch Ness monster

Is there a strange creature lurking in the depths of Loch Ness? Many people claim to have seen a prehistoric monster swimming in the lake. Some people say this is a hoax, but the scientists are still searching. They have found nothing – yet . . .

An oil-drilling platform off the Scottish coast

Highland cattle beneath Ben Cruachan

Islands and coasts

Scotland's western coastline is ragged, protected from the open Atlantic by the Western Isles. These include the scattered chains of the Inner and Outer Hebrides. Smallholders called crofters live by farming, fishing, peat-cutting, or producing textiles.

Across the stormy waters from Cape Wrath and John o' Groats lie the Orkneys and the distant Shetlands. These northern islands were once settled by Vikings from Scandinavia.

The chief towns of eastern Scotland are Dundee, on the River Tay, and the fishing port of Aberdeen. Oil has brought wealth to the northeastern region since the 1970s, when oilrigs and platforms were first built offshore, in the North Sea.

London

London, in England, is the capital and centre of government for the United Kingdom. Its Houses of Parliament stand beside the River Thames, beneath a tall clock tower, known as Big Ben. Nearby is No.10 Downing Street, the home of Britain's Prime Minister, or head of government.

The people of Britain vote for their members of Parliament. This system of government is called a democracy. Britain is also a monarchy, ruled by a queen or king. When in London, the monarch lives at Buckingham Palace. Soldiers wearing tall fur hats, called bearskins, guard the palace.

Central London is actually made up of two ancient cities which are now joined together. The older of the two, the City of London, was once surrounded by stone walls. It contains the huge cathedral of St Paul's, designed by Sir Christopher Wren. Today the city is an international centre of banking and business. The other ancient city, the City of Westminster, lies to the west. It takes in Westminster Abbey and the Houses of Parliament. Its busy shopping streets, theatres and cinemas are referred to as London's 'West End'.

The Greater London area takes up 1580sq km (610sq miles) and is home to more than 6 775 000 people.

St. Paul's Cathedral and the City of London lie close to the River Thames.

Sights to see

Tower of London – This grim castle was built more than 900 years ago. Many famous traitors had their heads cut off here in the old days. The Tower is still guarded by Yeomen Warders ('Beefeaters') who wear uniforms of red or blue. The Crown Jewels of England can be seen here.

Greenwich – A boat trip down the River Thames takes visitors past former docks to the site of the National Maritime Museum and the *Cutty Sark*, a fine 1869 clipper ship.

Museums – Other famous museums lie to the west. The British Museum, in Bloomsbury, displays many treasures from ancient Egypt and Rome. The Natural History section, in Kensington, has wonderful exhibits of dinosaurs.

Trafalgar Square – Tourists gather beneath Nelson's Column to look at the fountains and feed the pigeons. The National Gallery is on the square's north side.

Madame Tussaud's (founded 1835) – Visit Marylebone to see amazingly lifelike wax figures – heroes and heroines, villains and celebrities.

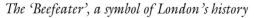

The 'Beefeater', a symbol of London's history

The Notting Hill carnival, celebrating Caribbean culture

A city patchwork

Central London is linked to the suburbs by an underground railway known as the 'Tube'. It was the world's first, begun in 1863. At street level there are red double-decker buses and black taxis.

Londoners are often called 'Cockneys'. True Cockneys were once said to be born 'within the sound of Bow bells'. Today, of course, London has spread far beyond the district of Bow, absorbing other towns and villages. However, many of these areas still keep their separate identities.

Immigrants have settled in London since before the Middle Ages. They have come from Europe, Asia, Africa and the Caribbean. All have added to the life and culture of London, making it a truly international city.

People at work

More than half of Britain's workers are employed in service industries. Many workers are employed in the tourism or leisure industries and work in hotels or restaurants. Others work in stores and shops, in banks or insurance companies. London is an international centre of finance. Its business district, home of the Bank of England and the Stock Exchange, is known simply as 'the City'.

As a member of the European Community (EC), Britain forms part of a 'single market' with other European nations. Goods may be exported and imported freely within this market.

Some of the greatest inventors in history were born in Britain, and the nation was once the world's greatest

Lloyd's building, in the City of London

A chemical plant in the northeast of England

industrial power. Today, many mines, shipyards and factories have been closed down. New companies, some of which are internationally owned, have taken their place. Car manufacturing and electronics are major industries in the Great Britain of the 1990s.

Modern industries are often cleaner than the old ones. The air of London, 'The Smoke', was once thick with industrial smog, and the River Thames was filthy. Today, both air and water are less polluted.

Great Britain has reserves of coal, oil and natural gas. These are all used to fuel power stations, alongside hydroelectric and nuclear sources. Research is also being carried out into wind and tidal power.

On the land

Farming varies greatly from one region to another. Hill farms breed sheep for wool and meat. Dairy and beef herds are to be found on lowland farms. Farms also produce pigs, chickens, turkeys and fish such as trout. Crops include wheat, barley, oats, potatoes, sugar beet and oilseed rape. Farming has changed greatly in recent years. Much more food is produced using far fewer people. Only two per cent of the labour force now work on the land. Farming, forestry and fishing are closely tied to the needs and policies of other EC members.

A prize-winning Welsh black bull

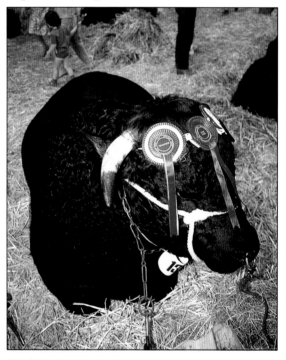

Jobs and wages

Britain, like most of Western Europe, enjoys a high standard of living. However, there are also economic and social problems, and in some regions large numbers of people are jobless. The pay and working conditions of many employees are protected by trade unions. Women make up over 40 per cent of the labour force.

Everyday life

The suburbs of most towns and cities have rows of semi-detached houses like these.

A train journey through Britain shows the visitor many different kinds of housing. In the cities, there are high-rise tower blocks built in the 1960s and small red-brick terraced houses dating from about a hundred years ago.

In the suburbs there may be rows of small houses built in pairs. These 'semi-detached' houses often have well-tended gardens. Many people like to spend their weekends looking after their gardens. New towns were built during the 1960s, and large 'council estates' contain housing rented from the local authority.

Out in the countryside, the styles of housing vary greatly according to the region. Cottages may be built from local stone, brick or timber. Roofs may be tiled, slated or thatched with reed.

There are still many unspoiled historical villages in Britain. There are ancient churches and castles, and magnificent mansions known as 'stately homes'. Some of these are still owned by descendants of the families which built them long ago. Others are now publicly owned and are open to visitors.

Shopping in a street market in London

Shops and markets

In many towns the main shopping area is called the High Street. Here, small, locally-owned shops may still be seen. However, more and more stores are owned by national chains. Often modern shopping centres have been built. This has made many town centres look alike.

Away from the town centres, small 'corner shops' provide groceries out of normal shopping hours. As elsewhere in Europe, more and more people buy their weekly supplies at large out-of-town supermarkets.

In both town and country there are busy street markets on certain days. The weekend is a favourite time for bargain-hunting at jumble sales and car-boot sales, where second-hand goods and bric-a-brac may be found.

A fair society?

Good health care and education are provided free throughout Britain. However, there are also privately run hospitals and schools. Confusingly, some of the best-known private schools are called 'public schools'!

Many faiths

In England, the official, or 'established', faith is that of the Christian Protestant Church of England (Anglican). The Church in Wales, also Anglican, is no longer established. Many people worship at Baptist, Presbyterian or Calvinist chapels. The Presbyterian Church of Scotland is established north of the border. Britain is home to many other Christians, from Roman Catholics to Quakers. There are also Jews, Hindus, Sikhs and Muslims, who worship at synagogues, temples and mosques. Many British people follow no religious faith.

A Roman Catholic church at Cille Choirill, in Scotland

Food and drink

Day starts with breakfast. Traditionally, this is made up of eggs and bacon. It may also include sausages, black pudding, fried bread, mushrooms or tomatoes! However, on a busy weekday, most people have only a piece of toast and marmalade, or a bowl of cereal and a cup of tea. The British drink large amounts of tea throughout the day and also fresh or instant coffee. The main meal of the day may be meat and gravy, fish or chicken, served with vegetables and followed by a dessert. It may be served as lunch (at about 1pm) or as dinner (at about 8pm). The third meal (lunch, or supper if eaten at about 6pm) is lighter, and quickly prepared.

Traditionally, the main meal of the week was Sunday lunch. This was a gathering for all the family. Fewer people now follow this routine, and still fewer serve another meal that was once popular – afternoon tea, with sandwiches, cakes and biscuits.

Eating out

Traditional British cooking, such as roast beef or leg of lamb with roast potatoes, is hearty and filling. Britain is known for its game, pies and puddings, but many of these dishes are now rarely served. Food today is often lighter and healthier. Many

A traditional English breakfast

Fish and chips, food for the street

people now eat vegetarian meals, without any meat.

Many people enjoy eating out at French, Italian or Greek restaurants. Almost every town has Indian and Chinese restaurants, which are very popular and offer good value.

Take-away food includes American-style hamburgers as well as a fine British invention – fish-and-chips served in paper, with salt, vinegar and pickled onions.

Each area of Britain has its own special foods and dishes. English cheeses include Stilton, Cheddar, Cheshire, Gloucester, Red Leicester and Sage Derby. There are Cumberland sausages, and Yorkshire puddings made of batter and soaked in gravy. London is known for shellfish (cockles and winkles), and for jellied eels served with mashed potatoes and peas. Cornwall has meat pies called 'pasties' and thick clotted cream.

Wales offers Caerphilly and other cheeses, welshcakes, sea trout and 'laverbread', a seaweed fried with oats and bacon. Scotland is known for its salmon, grouse, venison and haggis, a dish made of minced offal and oatmeal.

In the pub

English beers include bitters, milds, stouts and lagers. Scotland is the home of fine whisky, especially the famous malt varieties. Adults may drink any of these in a public house, or 'pub'.

Some English pubs are more than 1000 years old! The pub is an important meeting place in both town and country. Here people may gossip, argue, sing, play darts or eat a snack. Many pubs serve hot meals for working people at lunchtime. Some may also have rooms and gardens for families to use at weekends.

The pub is at the centre of village life.

Leisure and arts

Many of the world's great sports were first played in the British Isles. Association football (known as 'soccer' or simply 'football') is played throughout Britain. World-famous teams include Tottenham Hotspur, Arsenal, Liverpool, Manchester United, and Celtic and Rangers from Glasgow. Another type of football, called Rugby Union, is played with particular passion in Wales, and Rugby League is popular in Yorkshire and Lancashire.

Cricket is England's chief summer sport. An international or 'test' match can last up to five days. Important dates in the sporting calendar include the Wimbledon tennis championships and the regattas at Henley (for rowing) and Cowes (for sailing). Famous horseracing courses include Newmarket, Epsom and Cheltenham.

Many people watch their favourite sports, such as snooker, on television. Most homes in Britain also have videos, and films are often hired or bought to watch at home. Personal computers are very popular and are used for fun, such as playing computer games, as well as for more serious activities.

Musical Britain

British pop stars have been famous around the world ever since the 1960s. Wales and Scotland have a lively pop and folk scene. Songs are recorded in Welsh and Scots Gaelic as well as in English. Regional instruments include the bagpipes of Scotland, Ireland and Northumbria and the harp of Wales.

Liverpool fans celebrate at the Football Association's Cup Final.

The Welsh National Opera perform Falstaff

Classical music, opera and ballet are probably more popular than ever before. Famous British composers include Henry Purcell (1659-95), Edward Elgar (1857-1934) and Benjamin Britten (1913-76).

Art galleries

A visit to the galleries of London, Cardiff, Glasgow or Edinburgh will introduce the visitor to many great artists. Allan Ramsay (1713-1784), portraitist, was brought up in the High Street of Edinburgh and became the King's Painter. William Blake (1757-1827) painted strange, personal visions. John Constable (1776-1837) recorded the beautiful English countryside. JMW Turner (1775-1851) mastered the painting of light on great swirling canvases. Gwen John (1876-1939) showed the intensity of life in quiet scenes.

An island of writers

The English language has been celebrated by some of the world's greatest writers, such as Geoffrey Chaucer (c1342-1400) and William Shakespeare (1564-1616). Great English novelists include Jane Austen (1775-1817), George Eliot (1819-80) and Charles Dickens (1812-70).

The variants of English spoken in Scotland and Wales influenced the fine poetry of Hugh MacDiarmid (1892-1978) and Dylan Thomas (1914-53). There are also wonderfully rich literatures in both Scots Gaelic and Welsh.

Festival time

Britain's chief public holidays are at Christmas and Easter. New Year's Eve, or Hogmanay, is a special celebration in Scotland. Bonfires and fireworks on 5 November recall Guy Fawkes and his conspirators, who attempted to blow up the English Parliament in 1605. Many festivals and pageants date back to pre-Christian times. Some feature 'Morris dances' with bells and sticks or stag dances with antler head-dresses.

Up-Helly-Aa commemorates Viking rule in the Shetlands.

Back into history

The sun rises at Stonehenge, in Wiltshire.

Great Britain was originally joined to the European mainland. The River Thames flowed into the River Rhine. Prehistoric hunters must have entered the region at a very early date. Human remains found at Swanscombe, Kent, may be 400 000 years old.

Through the ages there have been many changes in climate and vegetation. The region became covered in ice and was roamed by woolly mammoths and rhinoceroses. From about 15 000 years ago the sea level began to rise as the Arctic ice caps melted. About 8000 years ago Great Britain became an island.

New people arrived in Britain over the years, bringing with them the knowledge of crop-growing, livestock-raising and metalworking. The massive pillars of Stonehenge, raised between about 2800 and 1400 BC, are still to be seen on Salisbury Plain, in Wiltshire.

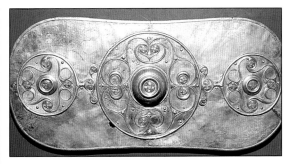

A bronze shield used by British Celts

Celts and Romans

The Celts were particularly skilled in metalworking. Their culture spread outwards from Central Europe from about 800 BC onwards. Celtic tribes called Britons lived in Great Britain, and other Celts called Gaels occupied Ireland. They both lived by farming and raising cattle. They were famed for their finery and their bravado.

However, the Celtic warriors were no match for the well-organised armies of Rome. Great Britain was attacked in 55-54 BC and was finally invaded in AD 43. Southern Britain became part of the vast Roman Empire, but Ireland and northern Scotland remained free. The Romans built two wall defences to keep out fierce northern peoples, such as the Picts. Roman engineers built roads and fine cities such as Colchester (*Camulodunum*) and London (*Londinium*).

Angles and Saxons

Roman power collapsed in the fifth century AD, when the Roman soldiers left Britain. For some time the coasts of Britain had been attacked by fierce warriors. Gaels (called 'Scots') now poured into western Scotland. Angles, Saxons and Jutes attacked and settled southeastern England.

The Britons fought these invaders fiercely. The story of their struggle has come down to us in the legends of King Arthur. Gradually the Anglo-Saxon invaders seized most of England and set up small kingdoms. However, the Christian kingdoms of the Britons and the Gaels held their own in Scotland, Ireland and Wales.

Jorvik

A museum at York recreates the world of the Vikings, the Scandinavian sea-raiders who invaded large areas of the British Isles in the ninth and tenth centuries. Christian monks prayed in vain to be saved from the 'fury of the Northmen'.

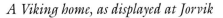

A Viking home, as displayed at Jorvik

Wars and revolts

In 1066 the Anglo-Saxons were finally defeated by William, Duke of Normandy. He was descended from Vikings who had settled in France. William granted lands in England to his followers, who were soon attacking parts of the north, Scotland, Ireland and Wales.

There were many clashes between powerful lords called barons and the Kings of England. A treaty called Magna Carta, signed in 1215, limited the powers of the English King. Between 1095 and 1291 many knights from Great Britain joined in a series of holy wars. These campaigns were fought by Christians against the Muslims in the Near East, and were called the Crusades.

Mediaeval England became a powerful nation. It ruled large areas of France, which led to long wars on the European mainland. There was also fighting at home. Poor peasants rose in revolt against their rulers in 1381.

United or divided

The English kings tried to conquer Wales and Scotland. They met with strong resistance.

Wales was united under the rule of Llywelyn Fawr ('the Great', 1173-1240). His grandson, Llywelyn ap Gruffudd, was killed by the English in 1282 and Edward I gained control over Wales. In Scotland, Robert, called 'the Bruce',

The Bayeux tapestry tells the story of how the Normans invaded England.

Robert the Bruce, leader of the Scots

However, by this time a Welsh family, the Tudors, ruled England.

Famous Tudor rulers included Henry VIII (1491-1547), who married six times. Henry challenged the Pope's power in England. This led to the development of the Protestant Anglican Church. Henry's daughter Elizabeth I (1533-1603) fought against Catholic Spain which sent a fleet, or Armada, to invade England in 1588.

Elizabeth I had no children, so the English throne passed to her cousin, James VI of Scotland (1566-1625). Political union followed in 1707.

Roundheads and Cavaliers

In 1642 civil war broke out in England and Wales. The armies of Parliament, under Oliver Cromwell (1599-1658), defeated King Charles I, who was executed in 1649. The monarchy was not restored to power until 1660.

One of the battles of the English Civil War is re-enacted.

defeated a large English army at Bannockburn in 1314. Scotland remained independent.

Wales was finally defeated in 1413, after a long war of independence led by Owain Glyndŵr. The political union of England and Wales followed in 1536-43.

Into the modern world

In 1714 the British throne passed to a German family, the royal house of Hanover. Rebellions against Hanoverian rule were defeated in Scotland in 1715 and 1745-6.

During the eighteenth century Britain began to lead the world in developing new technology and industry. Canals were built, steam engines developed, and coal was mined. The 1800s saw the world's first railways, and an 'industrial revolution' was now under way. Country people left the land to work in factories in the growing cities.

Many goods were exported overseas, for Britain was now at the centre of a worldwide empire. Although it lost much

Horse-drawn carriages gave way to trains, as the Stockton to Darlington railway opened in 1825.

of its North American territory in 1777, the British Empire still came to include Canada, India, Australia and New Zealand, as well as many lands in the Caribbean, in Africa and in the Pacific. Queen Victoria (1819-1901) ruled over the largest empire the world has ever seen.

Ireland was part of the United Kingdom from 1800 until 1921, but life there was very hard. Many people died of famine. Scottish and Welsh families joined the flood of poor Irish people who left their homes to settle overseas.

British troops fight in the First World War.

Two world wars

Between 1914 and 1918 the United Kingdom fought a war against its chief rivals, Germany and Austria-Hungary. Britain's allies included France, Russia and, from 1917, the United States. Many troops came from the lands of the British Empire. Nearly ten million soldiers died during the First World War.

By 1939 Britain was again at war with Germany and fighting for survival. By its end in 1945 the war had spread around the world, involving every continent. As many as 55 million people may have died as a result of this Second World War.

Britain into Europe

Exhausted by its victory in the war, Britain set about rebuilding its bombed cities. The 1951 Festival of Britain offered people the vision of a bright future. There were to be many changes. A 'welfare state' was set up to create a

fairer society. Overseas, many British colonies became independent. Many joined the Commonwealth, an international organisation, but the days of empire were finally over. Britain now looked to Europe, joining the EC in 1973.

Issues of today

What questions are being discussed in Britain in the 1990s?
– Should the EC become a political as well as an economic union?
– How can unemployment be tackled?
– Is there a future for the monarchy?
– Is there a solution to the problems of Northern Ireland? The British-governed province has seen violence for 25 years.
– Should England, Scotland and Wales become separate nations within the EC?
– Should the environment be kept cleaner and greener?

Britain in Europe

Fact file

United Kingdom

Today's Union Flag (or 'Jack') dates back to 1801. Its design shows the English and Scottish flags combined with a former Irish flag, the Saltire of St Patrick. The national anthem is 'God Save the Queen (or King)'. The UK currency is the 'pound sterling' (£). £1 is divided into 100 pence (p).

England

The English flag is the Cross of St George, red on a white field. St George's day (23 April) is the national day. The national emblem is a rose. Unofficial anthems include *Land of Hope and Glory* and the hymn *Jerusalem*.

Wales

Today's Welsh flag was not officially recognised until 1958. However, its Red Dragon may date back to Roman times. The national day (St David's Day or *Gŵyl Ddewi*) is 1 March. The Welsh emblem is a leek or a daffodil. The national anthem is *Hen Wlad fy Nhadau* ('Land of my Fathers').

Scotland

The official flag of Scotland is the Saltire of St Andrew, white on dark blue. A Red Lion flag is also widely flown. St Andrew's day is celebrated on 30 November and the Scottish emblem is a thistle. Unofficial anthems include *Scotland the Brave* and *Oh, Flower of Scotland*.

In Parliament

The chief political parties in Great Britain are the Labour Party, the Conservative Party and the Liberal Democrats. There is a general election at least every 5 years.

News and broadcasting

Famous UK newspapers include *The Times*, *The Guardian* and the *Daily Telegraph*. More popular papers such as the *Sun* or *Daily Mirror*, have a smaller, 'tabloid' format. There are also regionally produced daily newspapers such as the *Yorkshire Post* and *The Scotsman*.

The British Broadcasting Corporation (BBC) provides many national television and radio programmes, paid for by a licence fee. There are also local and commercial stations, some broadcasting in the language of the local community as well as English. Britain has four main television channels in addition to satellite and cable services.

Education

By law, children must go to school until they are 16 years old. When they are about five they go to Primary School. At about 11 they go on to Secondary School. At 16 they take their General Certificate of Secondary Education (GCSE) or Scottish Certificate of Education examinations. For some students, A-level or Higher Grade courses lead on to a university education. In some areas there are sixth-form colleges for pupils aged 16-18.

Some famous people

Boudicca (d.AD60) was a Celtic Queen who led the British tribes in a revolt against the Romans

Alfred the Great (849-899) was the Anglo-Saxon King of Wessex

Llywelyn Fawr (1173-1240) united large areas of Wales

William Wallace (c1270-1305) was a fighter for Scottish independence

Dafydd ap Gwilym (c1320-80) was the greatest poet in the Welsh language

Christopher Wren (1632-1723) was a famous architect

Isaac Newton (1642-1727) was a scientist and mathematician

James Watt (1736-1819) was a pioneer of steam power

Isambard Kingdom Brunel (1806-59) was an engineer and shipbuilder

Charles Darwin (1809-82) was a naturalist

Florence Nightingale (1820-1910) was a founder of nursing

Emmeline Pankhurst (1858-1928) campaigned for women's rights

Winston Churchill (1874-1965) was a statesman and prime minister

John Logie Baird (1888-1946) was the pioneer of television

Christopher Sydney Cockerell (1910-) invented the hovercraft

Margot Fonteyn (1919-91) was a world famous ballerina

Margaret H Thatcher (1925-) became the first woman prime minister of Britain

David Hockney (1937-) is a famous painter

Some key events in history

AD43: the Roman invasion of Britain

406: the Romans left Britain

844: Kenneth MacAlpin became King of Picts and Scots

1016: Danish King Knut (Canute) became King of England

1066: William of Normandy defeated Harold II at Hastings and the Norman invasion of Britain began

1095: the start of the First Crusade

1215: the signing of the Magna Carta agreement between the king and the nobles

1314: the Scots defeated the English at Bannockburn

1348-49: Black Death in Britain killed millions of people

1400: the Welsh attacked the English under the leadership of Owain Glyndŵr

1415: Henry V of England defeated the French at Agincourt

1588: the Spanish Armada was defeated by the English navy

1642-49: the Civil War between Parliament and the king

1707: the Act of Union united England and Wales with Scotland

1776: American colonists declared independence from Britain

1815: Britain defeated France at the battle of Waterloo

1914-18: First World War

1939-45: Second World War

1952: Elizabeth II was crowned as Queen of the United Kingdom

1973: Britain joined the European Community (EC)

Index

Aberdeen   13
arts   12, 22, 23
Atlantic Ocean   5, 10, 13

Bath   10
Birmingham   8
Bristol   10

Cambridge   7
canals   8, 28
Canterbury   6
Cardiff   11, 23
castles   9, 11, 15, 18
Celts   9, 10, 25
Channel Islands   7
churches   18, 19
Clyde, River   12
coal mining   9, 11, 17, 28
Cornwall   10, 21
Crusades   26

Dover   7
Dundee   13
Durham   9

East Anglia   7
Edinburgh   12, 23
English Channel   5
European Community (EC)   5, 16, 17, 29, 31

farming   6, 7, 10, 13, 17, 24, 25
festivals   23
fishing   9, 10, 13, 17
flags   11, 30
food   17, 20, 21

Glasgow   12, 23
government   11, 14, 30

housing   18

industry   8, 9, 11, 17, 28
Isle of Man   9
Isle of Wight   7

kings   14, 25, 26, 27, 31

language   9, 11, 12
Liverpool   9
Loch Ness   13
London   6, 14, 15, 16, 17, 21, 23, 25

Manchester   9
Mersey, River   9
Midlands   8
museums   12, 15

North Sea   5, 6, 13
Nottingham   8

oil   11, 13, 17
Oxford   6, 7

Pennines   8
ports   7

queens   14, 27, 28, 31

railways   5, 9, 15, 28
religion   19, 26
roads   6, 8, 25
Romans   10, 25, 31

Salisbury Plain   7, 24
Shakespeare, William   8, 23
shipbuilding   9, 12, 17
shopping   14, 19
Snowdon   11
South Downs   6
sport   22
steel   11
Stonehenge   24
Stratford-upon-Avon   8

Thames, River   6, 14, 15, 17, 24
Trent, River   8
Tudors   27

Vikings   13, 25, 26

wars   25, 26, 27, 29

York   9, 25